Here are two friends.
Two friends play tag.

Here are three
friends. Three friends
slide down.

COUNTING
MY FRIENDS

by Julian Ramirez
illustrated by Beth O'Grady

⬲Harcourt

Orlando   Boston   Dallas   Chicago   San Diego

Visit *The Learning Site!*

www.harcourtschool.com

Here is one friend.
One friend waves
a flag.

Here are four friends.
Four friends ride
around.

Here are five friends.
Five friends play in
the sand.

Here are six friends.
Six friends march in
a band.

Here are seven
friends. Seven friends
can splash.

Here are eight friends.
Eight friends pick up
trash.

Here are nine friends.
Nine friends kick
a ball.

Here are ten friends.
Ten friends paint
a wall.

How many friends do
I count today? Ten
friends come to play.